1 PETER 1 : 1-12

Sometimes it's really difficult!

The first letter of Peter was written to people who were fairly new Christians.

They were finding it hard to live for Jesus, and many people around them were giving them a hard time because of their faith.

Peter writes to encourage them to "stick at it"! He reminds them of the great things that God has done for them already, and he shows them the terrific future that God has planned for all those who remain faithful to him.

You belong to God !

So live like you belong to him!

Let's get started

Chapter 1
Verses 1 – 2

1. Who wrote this letter? (1:1) _____

2. Who is this letter written to? (1:1) _____

_____

3. What are some of the things that verse 2 tells us about what it means to belong to God's people? _____

_____

_____

_____

4. What has God already done for us? (1:3)

_____

_____

5. What can we look forward to? (1:3-4)

_____

_____

6. Sometimes we can't see all the blessings that God has for us. Why does he keep them for us in heaven? (1:4)

_____

_____

_____

THINKSPOT

7. What do you think are some of these "blessings" that God has in store for you?

8. What else is God keeping safe? (Look carefully at verse 5.) _____

_____

_____

9. Why does God sometimes allow us to suffer as Christians? (1:6-7)

_____

_____

_____

10. If we stand up to these difficulties in this life, what will be the result? (end of verse 7)

_____

_____

_____

11. When things aren't going well, it can be really hard to keep on going as a Christian. So even though we can't always see how God is helping us, what can we always be thankful and joyful about? (1:8-9)

_____

_____

_____

THINKSPOT

When you read what God has promised for the future, how does it help you to understand and deal with your present problems?

Think it Through

12. What are the things that sometimes make it really hard for you to be a Christian?

13. Describe a time when you felt like giving up being a Christian.

14. What things did you find in this study which will help you get through these difficult times in the future?

1 PETER 1:13-2:3

*D*o I really
have to change
my life?

"Let's have a look at some of the ways that my life is meant to change now that I belong to God!"

How should I change?

1. What are some of the ways that you can really show that you are living for God?

   a) verse 13 _____

   _____

   _____

   b) verse 14 _____

   _____

   _____

   c) verses 15-16 _____

   _____

   _____

   d) verse 17 _____

   _____

   _____

THINKSPOT

2. Take ONE of your answers to question 1, and write down a practical example of how you can put that into action in your day to day life.

3. What price did God pay to set you free from your old non-Christian life? (1:18-19)

_____
_____
_____
_____

4. What other things can you learn about Jesus from verses 20 and 21?

_____
_____
_____
_____

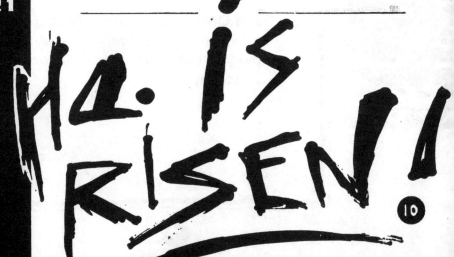

HE IS RISEN!

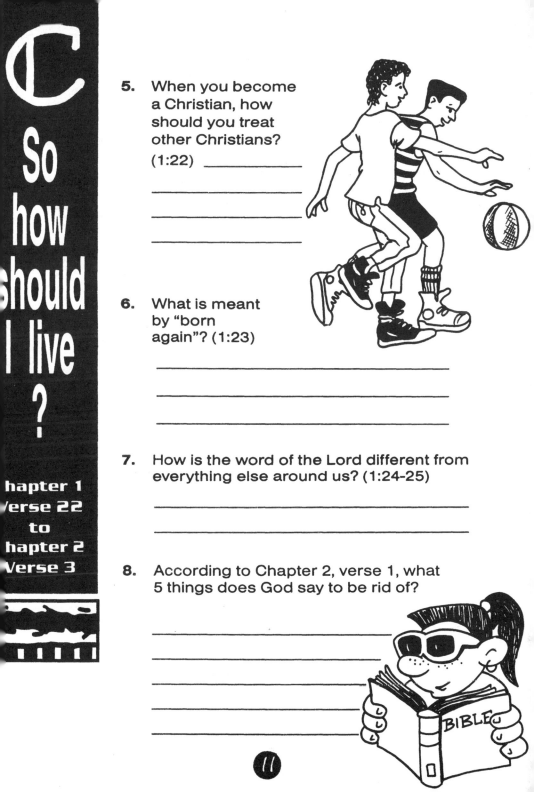

C

So how should I live?

5. When you become a Christian, how should you treat other Christians? (1:22) _____

_____

_____

_____

6. What is meant by "born again"? (1:23)

_____

_____

_____

7. How is the word of the Lord different from everything else around us? (1:24-25)

_____

_____

8. According to Chapter 2, verse 1, what 5 things does God say to be rid of?

_____

_____

_____

_____

_____

11

THINKSPOT

9. Take ONE of your answers from Question 8, and answer these two questions about it:

(a) Here is an example of where I'm tempted to do this sin:

(b) Here is something specific that I can do to help me get rid of this sin from my life:

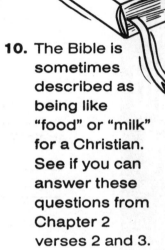

slurp slurp

munch

munch

10. The Bible is sometimes described as being like "food" or "milk" for a Christian. See if you can answer these questions from Chapter 2 verses 2 and 3.

a) What should your attitude be to the Bible?

_____

_____

b) What will the Bible do for you?

_____

_____

c) As you do this, what will you discover?

_____

_____

Think it Through

11. What could you do so that the Bible will have more impact in changing your life?

12. Write down one thing that you have learned from this study that will change your life.

3

1 PETER 2: 4-10

*W*hat difference does Jesus make?

1. How is Jesus described in verse 4?
   What do you think this means?

   _____

   _____

   _____

2. We Christians are also told to become like
   'stones'. (verse 5) When we come
   together, what sort of a building will the
   'stones' make? _____

   _____

   _____

3. In verse 5 we are described as a 'spiritual
   house'. What does Peter mean by this?
   What is meant to happen in a 'spiritual
   house'? _____

   _____

   _____

THINKSPOT

4. What sort of a "sacrifice" can I offer to God?
   (Romans 12:1 might help you!)

5. Read verses 6 to 8.

a) What sort of 'stone' is Jesus?

_____
_____
_____
_____
_____
_____
_____

b) What promises are given for those who believe in him?

_____
_____
_____
_____
_____

c) What effect will this 'stone' have on those who don't believe in Jesus? _____

_____
_____
_____

THINKSPOT

6. How does this information affect the way you live?

7. Jesus has made us into a new group of people – his family of Christians. List the 4 ways that this new group of people is described in verse 9.

_____

_____

_____

_____

_____

_____

_____

8. If God has made us into this new group of people, what are we now meant to do? (verse 9)

_____

_____

_____

9. Now that God has made us into his new group of people, what changes have happened to us? (verse 10) _____

_____

_____

10. Look back at verses 9-10, and jot down your own thoughts about these questions:

a) What difference is Jesus making to the sort of person that I am?

b) What difference is Jesus making to the sort of things that I do?

4

1 PETER 2: 11-25

Can't I just do what I like?

How do you feel when someone pushes you around and tells you what to do?

1. What are we warned not to give in to? (2:11)

_____
_____
_____
_____
_____

THINKSPOT

2. As a Christian, what are some of the wrong things that you find it easy to give in to?

Temptation

3. What is a good reason for making sure we live the way God wants? (2:12) _____
_____
_____

Christ has set us free – but he calls upon us to live as "slaves" or "servants" serving both God and the people around us by the way we live.

"Live as free people; do not, however, use your freedom to cover up any evil, but live as God's slaves."
1 Peter 2:16

4. List the 4 ways that we are meant to be "servants" of each other in 2:17. Then give an example of how you can put that into action in your own life this week.

WHAT THE BIBLE SAYS	HOW I CAN PUT IT INTO ACTION

B

How much do I have to bear ?

Chapter 2 Verses 18 – 23

5. What does verse 18 teach us about what our attitude should be to those who are in authority over us? (e.g. parents, teachers, employers etc.)
(You might also get some clues from verses 13-14.)

_____
_____
_____
_____
_____
_____

THINKSPOT

6. Think of an example when you think someone has used their authority over you in a wrong way. How did you feel? What did you do about it?

7. If you're going to live as a Christian, sometimes you will end up "suffering as a servant". What example has Christ left for us to follow? (2:20-21)

_____

_____

8. What 5 things do you learn about Jesus in verses 22 and 23?

a) _____

b) _____

c) _____

d) _____

e) _____

How much did Jesus bear ?

Chapter 2
Verses 24 – 25

9. From verse 24:

a) What has Jesus done about our sins? _____

_____

_____

b) What result does this have for us? _____

_____

_____

c) What effects do Jesus' wounds have on you? What do you think this means?

_____

_____

_____

_____

10. From verse 25:

a) What were we like? _____

_____

_____

b) What has happened? _____

_____

_____

c) How is Jesus described?

_____

_____

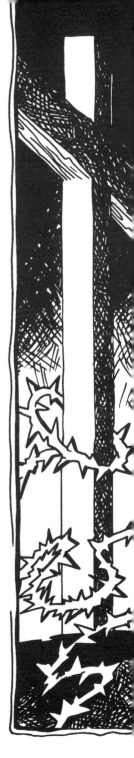

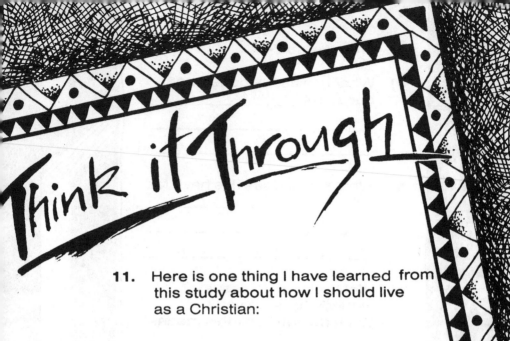

Think it Through

11. Here is one thing I have learned from this study about how I should live as a Christian:

12. Here is one thing that has "hit" me about what Jesus has done for me:

1 PETER 3: 1-12

*B*ut I want to have a good time!

In our last study, we looked at the question "Can't I Just Do What I Like?"

We saw how Christians are not meant to put themselves first, but to submit to people who have authority over them.

We saw how Jesus lived this out – even to the point of being put to death.

He showed us the real way to put other people first – even those who are hurting us – and he left us a great example to follow.

Today we will see how in our everyday personal relationships, we need to submit to God, and to submit to each other.

A Boy meets girl

Chapter 3
Verses
1 – 7

Peter writes these words to show us how husbands and wives are to treat each other. But we can also learn about everyday boy/girl relationships!

THINKSPOT

1. What sorts of things do girls normally do when they want to attract a bloke's attention and get him to like them?

2. According to verse 3, the Bible says that real beauty in a woman does not depend on: _____

_____

3. According to verse 4, the Bible says that real beauty depends on:

_____
_____
_____
_____

4. How did godly women make themselves beautiful in the past?

_____

_____

_____

Hey, you mean that all of us are meant to follow Jesus' example by serving the other people that we're in a relationship with?

5. If a wife becomes a Christian and her husband doesn't, what should she do? (verses 1-2)

_____

_____

_____

_____

_____

_____

_____

THINKSPOT

6. How do blokes these days normally treat their girlfriends?

7. According to verse 7, how are husbands really meant to treat their wives?

_____

_____

_____

THINKSPOT

8. How do you think that these verses relate to Galatians 3:28?

⚡33⚡

9. If we really are meant to live a life of submitting to others, what 4 ways does Peter show us for putting that into action?

v.8	
v.8	
v.8	
v.9	

10. What sorts of things do people normally think they have to do to "enjoy life" and have "good times"?

11. What does the Bible say you should do to "enjoy life" and see "good times"? (verses 10–11)

_____

_____

_____

_____

12. Why does living God's way produce a better life than disobeying him and doing wrong? (verse 12)

_____

_____

_____

_____

Think it Through

13. Here is one thing I've learnt about having a Christian boy/girl relationship:

14. Here is one thing I've learned about having a "good time" as a Christian:

15. Think of an occasion when you had a REALLY good time through being a Christian. What happened? What made it so good?

1 PETER 3:13-4:6

*W*hat if my friends don't believe?

It's not always easy to stand up for Jesus when your friends aren't Christians.

But Jesus wants you to hang in there with your non-Christian mates.

Maybe YOU will be the person who helps YOUR friends to start following Jesus!

How to talk about Jesus.

Chapter 3
Verses 13 – 17

THINKSPOT

1. How do you feel about talking to your non-Christian friends about Jesus? Describe a time when you should have said something, but you didn't.

2. Imagine you are writing a reply to someone who is having difficulty talking to their non-Christian friends about Jesus.

Re-write and summarise verses13-16 in your own words to show them the right way forward.

THINKSPOT

3. What are some of the things you can do to encourage others to ask you questions about your faith?

4. Rewrite verse 18 in your own words, to show what you think is the main message that we have to tell others.

_____

_____

_____

_____

_____

_____

_____

_____

_____

_____

_____

_____

5. What important point do the last few words of verse 21 and all of verse 22 add to our message about Jesus?_____

_____

_____

_____

6. If we really want to be obedient to Jesus, how should we live our earthly lives? (4:1-2)

_____

_____

_____

7. What activities were these people involved in before they became Christians? (4:3)

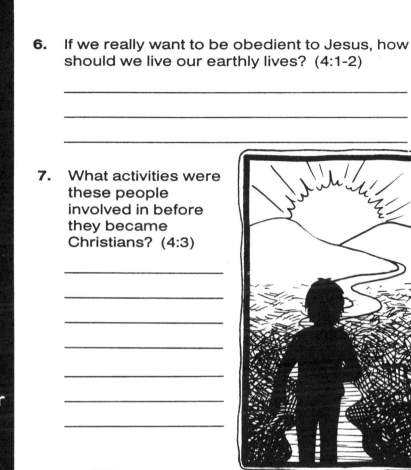

_____

_____

_____

_____

_____

_____

_____

THINKSPOT

8. What are some of the things that you used to do before you became a Christian which you've since given up?

9. How might non-Christians react when you no longer join in their wrong things? (4:4)

_____

_____

_____

10. What will happen to those who keep disobeying God? (4:5)

_____

_____

_____

Think it Through

11. Write down the names of one or two of your non-Christian friends.

Now write down what you can do THIS WEEK as a first step towards sharing your faith with them.

7

1 PETER 4 : 7-19

You mean I can help others ?

You don't just have to battle on by yourself if you're finding it difficult to be a Christian.

God has given you some special abilities – not just so you can "survive" – but he has given you abilities which can really help lead other people closer to him.

That's right – **you** have a part to play in strengthening other Christians and caring for your friends.

1. If "the end of all things is near", what are some of the things we should be doing that will really show that we belong to Jesus. (4:7-9)

_____

_____

_____

_____

_____

_____

2. Look carefully at Chapter 4, verse 10.

a) What has God given to every Christian?

_____

_____

_____

_____

b) How are we meant to use this gift for God?

_____

_____

_____

_____

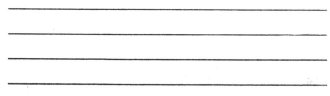

THINKSPOT

3. What special gifts or abilities do you think God has given to each of the people in your Bible study group?

Write each person's name down, and then try to think of at least 2 "gifts" that God has given them. (e.g. to play music, to lead Bible studies, to care for others etc.)

NAME	GIFTS

Share your answers in your group.

4. Now think of a way that you can put one of your OWN gifts into action THIS WEEK in a way that's going to help others.

_____

_____

IB

**The
ability
to
'stick
t out"**

hapter
4
erses
2 – 19

5. What can we learn about being
"knocked" because we are Christians?
(4:12)

_____

_____

_____

_____

6. How can you cope with being
"knocked" because you are a Christian?
What are some of the important things
to remember, and even be thankful for?
(4:13-16)

_____

_____

_____

_____

7. What is one final thing to remember
when you're finding it difficult to be a
Christian? (4:19)

_____

_____

_____

_____

Think it Through

8. How do you normally get "knocked" for being a Christian? Who normally does it? What do they "knock" you about? How do you feel when it's happening?

9. What might be a good way of handling it when you get "knocked" for being a Christian? How can you turn it into something that is positive?

10. How does it help you to know that God has given abilities to Christians to enable them to help each other?

1 PETER 5 : 1-14

*S*ticking at it ....together

THINKSPOT

1. Draw a picture or a diagram to symbolise what you think of "the church". Be imaginative! You could draw "the church" as a giant machine, like a person, ... or anything! Be creative! How can you symbolise what "the church" is really like? And make sure you include in your picture where **you** fit into "the church".

2. How should leaders in the church treat those in their care? (5:1-3)

_____

_____

_____

_____

3. As a younger person, how should you treat others in the church? (5:5-6)

_____

_____

_____

_____

THINKSPOT

4. What do you find hard about being involved with the church?

5. What are some of the advantages in being involved with your church?

6. What should you do when you are anxious or worried? (5:7)

_____
_____
_____
_____
_____
_____
_____
_____
_____
_____
_____

IB

When the devil tries to get me

Chapter 5 Verses 8 – 11

7. What are some of the things that you tend to worry about, that you should really be handing over to God?

8. How is the devil described in v.8?

_____
_____
_____
_____
_____
_____

THINKSPOT

9. What ways does the devil normally try to "get at" you? When do you usually tend to give in?

10. How should you deal with the devil when he attacks you? What should encourage you to remain firm? (5:9)

_____

_____

_____

11. What promise does God give that will help you no matter what hardships you face? (5:10)

_____

_____

_____

_____

Eternal Life!

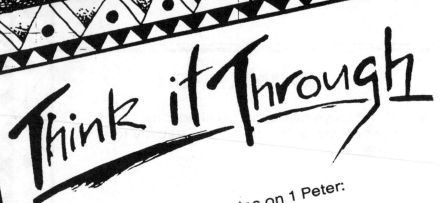

Think it Through

As you think through the series on 1 Peter:

12. What have you discovered about Jesus?

13. What have you discovered about God's promises?

14. What have you discovered about how to really stick at being a Christian?